Cat and Dog

Written by Jack Bell

Illustrated by Neil Sutherland, Blue-Zoo and Tony Trimmer

c-a-t, cat!

It is a cat.

d-**o**-**g**, dog!
It is a dog.

A cat and a dog!

It is a din.

c-**o**-**d**, cod!
It is a cod.

c-a-n, can!

It is a can.

Cat and dog dig in.